Freed Bird

ISBN 978-1-952320-33-0 (Paperback)
Freed Bird

This book is a work of fiction. Names, characters, places, events and incidents are totally the product of the author's imagination. Any resemblance to actual persons, events or locales, is entirely coincidental. Opinions expressed are entirely those of the author.

Yorkshire Publishing
4613 E. 91st St,
Tulsa, OK 74137
www.YorkshirePublishing.com
918.394.2665

Printed in the USA

Dancing from Flower to Fruit

Shavannah Angelique

TULSA

Contents

Dedication

Dedicated to my lovers and dreamers who dreamed a million things.

My life has been blessed with people who are filled with compassion and grit. I pieced this together for them because we all have something in common—we all grew from a place of pain. No matter their origin story or their war story, they all have seemed to grow into loving, heart filled, kind beings. I strive to embody the strength that my mother possesses. I aim to be as gracious as my soul sister. I marvel at how spontaneous and daring my brothers are. I question if I will ever be as fearless as my sister. Despite life's challenges, everyone that I hold dear to me is unprejudiced and unwavering, but even more so, open and accepting of life as it continues. This is for them. I see and admire their perseverance.

"We have these big beautiful brains and creative hands; how could we not make magic happen here? We were destined to touch something and create love with it and share it with the world. There's no way that with all this love that sits in our chest and waits to burst from the seams that we were put here to sit idly with it... how could we not be destined for more?"

Preface

I have always felt my life in random scraps of paper; meaning, that ever since I could remember, I used writing as an outlet. I experienced an uncommon childhood, and silence was always the way to keep what structure I had left intact. When I had uncertain or fear triggered feelings, I would write them in one of the many journals I collected. My pain and confusion manifested in forms of poetry and songs—despite never being able to carry a tune.

Then, one day, I wasn't able to write anymore. I just couldn't do it. There were no more words left in me. I was a young wife and soon to be a young mother of two beautiful children. For a total of ten years, my identity was fused with another being. From high school sweethearts to young love to mom and dad. So, I didn't need to write anymore because I had everything in front of me. I put my imagination to rest and lived my reality. Until one day, I couldn't write, even if I tried. To me, paper and pencil were just as much my home as the four walls that stood around me, but it felt like I was exiled and no longer able to visit the home built in words and phrases. It was as if my pain triggered my voice, and that voice was silenced because I was no longer hurting. A fair and beautiful trade.

As we grew together through many milestones, we saw past problems, or became halted by problems. There is one night, in particular, that I can't seem to forget. Of all the things I remember, and the million more memories that slip my mind, this evening replays in my head. A series of events played out this evening; while some moments were simultaneous, others were a rippling effect. We came about our seven-year itch slowly, as if a speed bump were in front of us, and then what felt like lost momentum, we just stopped. That night, I felt as though something changed and we started about a downward slope.

It was late into the evening and after a workday followed by a long class, he came home smelling like he had already had a few drinks. I, too, was exhausted from a long day working, tending to our two children, and tending to my own schoolwork. But this night was special, so I didn't fall asleep before he got home. It was our anniversary, but I didn't have a gift, as money would not allow such a gesture. But I had myself, a smile, and the words "happy anniversary". I was draped in a yellow t-shirt that was ten years old and pajama pants, but when he walked into our tiny bedroom, he said something that caused an upset in me. I felt embarrassed, ashamed, and guilty. His words replay in my mind as vividly as the look on his face. "You're not even naked," he scorned. His eyes were piercing, and his voice slightly raised. He was angry at me for not waiting for him in a certain way. He was angry at me for not doing more when I could have been angry at the fact that he didn't even remember our anniversary until I told him. But I did something wrong that night because I wasn't naked, waiting for him. Angrily, he left to go get another drink.

What happened next, I will take full blame for. I walked into the restroom and put on lingerie that did not feel nice to wear. I smeared lipstick on my frown, and I washed away my tears. After he came back home, a little more drunk than when he first arrived, I presented myself the way he imagined I would be that evening and I did what wives do on anniversaries. I say that I take the blame because I let someone else take a piece of me. Even if that someone was my husband. I was hurt by his words, but another thing happened that night, I was hurt by myself. I let myself down. I could have said "I'm too tired" or "not tonight". Surely, after seven years and two children together there would be some flexibility. I could have expressed my tears that night, but instead I concealed them. I didn't stick up for myself that night, but rather, I gave in. I bent at his will because I wanted to be a giving wife. So, I gave. Just as he was wrong to paint me with those words, I was wrong to allow it.

But I promised myself, after the split and after I sat with everything that continuously haunted me, that I would never give someone the ability to take a piece of me again. I would never let myself, hurting, give in to what someone else wants. I promised myself that I would always stick up for myself and be someone that I could count on.

The part that blows me away the most is that he didn't remember that night once he was sober, but I can't seem to forget it.

Over the years many things changed in my life, as things should. I went from young wife to young divorcee. The reasons that led up to my divorce were personal to me and familiar to many at the same time. Through these changes, I was cut wide open. I bled and cried and found my voice, again, a fair and beautiful trade.

I started pouring myself into these pages after separating with my husband. You will find that it is my own personal journey, but you may also find your own healing in it. I started a broken and shattered person. I doubted myself and my capabilities as a wife and a woman. I battled my anxiety and struggled not to go back on medication. My depression wanted to grab me. My shoulders slumped as I became increasingly defeated. You could see in my glossed over eyes that I was not okay; you could see my fragility and need for soothing.

With that, I also managed to pick myself back up. In starting my life over, I, and my children, moved in with my mother who lifted my chin when I said it was all my fault. She wiped my tears from beneath my puffy, wet eyes and said, "Don't do that, do not take his blame, do not let him say that it was your fault…" I saw my best friend as often as I could, and I cried to her. I listened to my brother's words and let myself feel comfort as they lifted me and made me feel safe. I sat and reconnected with my sister. I put fears to rest as I got to see my family, who spoke of my strength and my wit, which I had long forgotten about. With those, I would always be ok. I sat with myself. I learned what it means to love myself and from that blossomed a new woman. This imperfect, messy, emotional, guarded, but strong, humble, compassionate, and kind woman is who I want to present to the world. I am most proud of the fact that, despite all I have seen and endured, I remain open to possibility, life, and love.

This shaken, slightly battered soul is what I am comprised of, but I have given myself the forgiveness, time, and patience that I deserve. I have given myself the benefit of the doubt and the opportunity to see things as they are now. It is within this moment that I live, not thinking back to the past moments that once defined me. I am here, I am present, and I am living. I am shedding all that does not serve me, and I hope, more than anything, that you can too.

CHAPTER 1

Falling

Were your arms tied behind your back when someone reached their greed-stained fingers into the depths of your chest and wrapped them around your vulnerable heart? Did it hurt when they clenched their fist tighter, just because they could? There are times in our lives when people take things from us as we sit by and watch. There will be times when someone will get away with stealing the breath straight from your lungs and you won't be able to gasp loud enough to plead for help. It may not be a physical harm that you aim to flee. Maybe your mind has had enough, and your insecurities continue to bleed. It's possible to be with someone and all the while, you've lost your light and no longer smile. One day you're fine and the next day you can't breathe; one day you're in love and the next day you can't wait to leave. Your arms are tied behind your back, but to your knowledge you are being wrapped in a warm embrace. Little did you know, you were being robbed of your most precious and innate feelings. One day in love, the next, you're on a road to healing.

We let love touch our souls so that we have a chance at not feeling alone. Some days it feels easy to let people become our comfort zones so that we may walk with our heads a little bit higher than the day before. Sometimes we think to ourselves that no matter what happens today, there is someone who loves me at home to help me wash it all away. With great regret, we look past the red that stains their skin, but we do it anyway.

Love tasted like cigarettes whispering nicotine secrets to me in the form of a kiss. Its greeting was new, wrapped in familiar warmth. Reconciliation at the dawn of a new era. It was running full speed into his arms, in the dead of the night, and not caring about what would happen next. Love didn't ponder on the next step, but only on this very moment. This moment looked like a desperate plea to never be alone again on the brink of being alone for months on end. Love looked like it wanted to meet me and make a home out of me. So, I loved him. Oh, I loved until I couldn't love anymore.

In the "*I love you*" and "*forever*" that gets whispered in the cold of the night, we go blind to what aches in front of us at the excitement of the promise of warmth. Our senses dull and we endure more than we should bear, because that is the cost of love in this life of warfare. They know that your heart aches every time they pluck the feathers from your beautiful wings. He knows that when he says he's changed; it's another lie to add to the collection. Whiskey burns on his lips every time he gives you a kiss. But he says, "*I love you, I'm trying*", and the pain dulls to a numbness so he can stay. Lies leak from her mouth when she tells you you're the only one, but at night in bed, she feels like home. She feels safe and familiar, but her skin is different because it was touched by someone else. Her scent, now mixed with someone else's, doesn't render comfort anymore.

One day wakes us up and we realize that everything about ourselves that we loved—our light, our carefree smiles, our joy, and our craze—is gone, stolen away. When did love, so eager to meet us, become a stranger in our sheets? When did love, whispering sweet nothings, stop speaking to me? Silent treatment. When did love slow to a stop? I desperately miss the wind rushing through my hair when it ran at full speed. When did love feel more like a hot bleed? One day I woke up and realized that the person staring back at me was a stranger. I didn't know this face, covered in dark spots and stress-sunken eyes. The dried and broken hair atop my head was not mine. The dull, sad eyes, I did not recognize....

Terrible shame

It would be a terrible shame
If my heart never got to love you
The way it so desires
For I have dreamt of it a million different ways
Since the moment I tripped
And my eyes stumbled upon your smiling face

4 AM

What is 4 AM by your side?
Dusky embers cut through the dark
And light the edges of your jaw
Illuminating your sleeping smile
That wakens to kiss the top of my head
It is a slow, non-start

Because we don't rush to move
Off this island of a bed
Lost at sea
Waves are calm and soothing
We could sleep peacefully
Or pull waves as if we were the moon
Feel the island unsteady itself
I open myself to you
4 AM feels like tangled in the stars
Rough and magnificent, pleasant and ours

"I" is for...

"I" is for...
Impulsive, the way I am with my emotions
I act intensely and irrationally
But you'd never know it
Because I isolate myself
As to not intrude on your peace
Then when I feel fine
I show up, feeling indestructible
Even though I just spent an insurmountable
amount of time feeling insignificant
Impossible to tell me otherwise
Inquisitively asking about you
Hooked on every intricate word you say
I sit, incredulously, ignited by my own anger
Feeling insane by the end of the day
Irritated
Insomnia strikes again

J, K, L, M is for mad
The way I get when I get stuck on I

Two lovers

Two lovers
With deep darkened seas
Come together simply, like air blown through trees
Like leaves landing on the tops of lakes
Like you finding me
An embodiment of darkness
A black hole that sucked us in deep
Bumps and screams, gentle kissing
This is not meant to be
But love me so hard I forget to leave
Talk to me, let's smooth out the wrinkles of our pitch-black sheets
Not lie in wait, for everything to explode at our feet
Mirroring souls, the way we carry our hurt
Push people away, the way we bury in our dark
Open the blinds, we need to explore light
We've got lots of work to do
Should we decide to stay and fight
Is your hand meant for me
Should we walk, side by side, feet by feet

Red-handed

Caught me
Red handed
Blood dripping down my fingers
From the time I ripped my heart out
And gave it to you
Blindly and willingly
Too quickly
I gave all of me to you

When you spoke I gave you my mind
When our hands brushed, I gave you my time
When you laughed I gave you my heart
When you looked at me...
I burst at the seams and gave you everything that came out

I'm still learning to be selfish
I gave you something, that wasn't for giving
I need a full refund
Please, I'm begging

Skeptical Flowers

From skepticism, blooms questions
That were once seeded in the soil of my mind
But with sunshine and time
These nuisance thoughts sprout
And now crowd my mind
Like what ifs and one days
How much weight do your words carry
How deep are the things you feel or say
Are the pipe dreams I think up mine
Or do you feel the same
Would we ever melt into one another at the end of the day
Questions continuously bloom
Watered by the feelings I feel for you

Empty

I'm sorry for what you see when you look at me
My face will radiate joy
You see me and see a happy home
You see me and see love
Even though I'm cold to the bone
I'm sorry that it's all a lie
I'm sorry that my eyes are traps
You'll forever fall in the depths
Because it is empty and endless
When you get past the buildup of tears left unattended
You will see me
And you will find that I'm empty
And that it's all just a lie

Shattered

I am not broken
I am not broken
I am not broken
Said all the different pieces of her
In complete unison

So much so, that it was easy to pretend that only
one person stood firmly in conviction
So much so, that it sounded like it was just her
telling the world what she was not
Rather than all the pieces of her, once connected and whole
Now shattered and longing to be together again
Trying to convince her of something she felt wasn't real

Please don't make me

Tears well in the pockets of my eyes
Just begging please don't make me
Cause I'll do it
I'll drop everything I own to fix your smile
And everything I've known to seal cracks that
bear wounds deeper than a mile
Just please don't make me

Don't show me your eyes, big and hurt
Don't show me your troubles
How you've freed your heart, buried in cold dirt
Don't know that my heart loves to give
And don't ask how high
Cause I won't just jump, I will fly
To see you smile

Just please don't make me
Don't take my kindness as key
To whatever you want
Let me keep my walls intact
Painted big with black words
BOUNDARIES
I want to know you
And maybe love you
Give you the world when you earn it
But just don't take advantage of my heart
Please don't hurt it

Co-exist

I feel like I have been ripped into two different people
Walking hand in hand
Loving and holding each other through the day
Yet giving each other space to exist in their
own moments and in their own ways

One cries and feels like fallen flowers
The petals wilt and stems dried

The other burns intensely with rage
She sets fire to every step she takes

Together they are warm, the scent of daisies lingers through the day

Desperate love

Maybe the desperation for love
The cigarette butts
The "*I love you, but…*"
The '*yell to be heard*'
"Fuck you, you're not saying a word...
Please stay, I'll do better…
I promise this time,
Then we'll have forever…"
Is the type of love I deserved
Tainted with dishonesty
Contaminated trust
Manipulation of the mind
Sex between bodies
But no meeting of the mind
No greeting of the soul

Maybe this is the love
The only love I'll ever know

s.a.d.

S is for sulking
Sailing down slowly
Sheepishly present
Somewhat smiling
Shyly and quietly existing

A is for agitated
Aggravated and adamant
Aware of the pain
Always trying to justify
And just to come to the same point in time

D is for distant
Done
Deceased and damned
Damn

(unnamed)

My head is full
My thoughts are compounding
I can't breathe
My heart has no room
I need some grounding

I catch myself
I have been falling for too long
I notice my breathing is shallow
And my lungs ache from holding on

I can't stop crying
My anxiety is high
And I can't stomach fighting
My depression is too low

I hear your words echo
Painful little jabs that speak only to my soul
Small moments that now live, etched into my bones
The time I didn't yet know my depression, and you left
with words hanging, "I don't want to be around you"
The time you blamed your heavy drinking on my heavy sadness
The time your pain spoke for you and
called me a dirty, shady person
My eyes went dark, the words kept coming
And the words kept hurting
The times you thought it was okay to ask your wife,
who bore you two children, "Why are you so loose"
Or the time you got mad because I wasn't waiting naked
Sitting pretty and poised, like a shiny token

You punched a hole in the wall that I built a safe place in
You broke barriers with force
And in doing so
You pushed me away

Now I am hiding in plain sight
I am standing out in the open for no one to see
My heart is caged
Buried, under lock and key

This is my home

I was a shattered woman
I was an empty shell
Nothing inside to bear the walls of my person
So, when I took that last blow
I broke
I crumbled
I shattered

So, when you look at me and say
Let me help build you back up
I look at you, eyes wide
Do you think I'm dumb enough to give the man that broke me
The hammer to build me?
So, he can break me again?
This is my home
You are not welcome in

Done is me

Done is the woman who cannot breathe
Done is the woman who cannot see
Done is the woman whose heart aches and bleeds
Done is me

Read me

I think and feel best on paper
And in the past, it was a problem
But I'm learning that,
Maybe the problem was not that my vulnerability
was to be read, studied and learned
Instead, the problem is that I needed someone
who was willing to read me
But I had a visual learner
Who never quite could see me

Carvings

My memory bank is hard to access
But I remember clear as day
When your words felt so sharp
Like being covered in thick, red paint
My eyelids were weighed down
I couldn't see truth from lies
Just the red tint that shaded my lids, that blocked my cries
I lived a blue life in a city of red
I was deepened seas, trapped in our bed
I was the faded color purple
Washed away, no longer royalty
Those were things your words carved out of me

He knows

He knows too well
How to bend my soul
He knows how to fit his fist shaped words
Into my heart shaped whole
He knows that if he tears up
I lower my arms
Weapons down
Battle done
Tears cried... he won

He knows that my kindness
Can be taken for granted
Because he had taken
And taken
And taken
Without asking

He knows far too much
He knows far too well
So that's why it hurts so much more
When I feel bad for him
Cause I really feel bad for myself

But what he does not know
What he does not realize or see
Is that this past year
I changed
I died
And he killed me

So, all those things
I'm learning to stop doing
Instead, I am only living for me
Finding strength in my soul
Patching the walls of my heart
Allowing myself a brand-new start
Finding beauty in my kindness
Giving my love sparingly
To those who are worthy

Panic attack

Heat strikes deep in my core
I have to get out
I can't be here anymore
Run downstairs, hang a right
Sit off, far to the side
Where no one can see
I can't breathe
Heavy sinking chest begins to plague me
If I can run
I can escape these feelings
I can out pace these tears that begin to escape me
Distance myself a little further
Fast-paced feet carry me down the street
Chest starts burning
Lean against a tree
Close your eyes
Find your breathing
Wipe your face
Find your grace
Walk upstairs
Finish the day

I am an anchor to keep my family steady in one place and at the same time, I am stuck. You can't picture the world with heavy, bounding chains. I'm not love prepared on a clean slate. I am young but not fresh. I am a pen, worn down, ink used by other hands. They touch the surface and get dirt beneath their nails; they dig just enough to get me open. Just enough to decide to walk away before they feel swallowed. I'm like a monster that everyone is smart enough to steer clear of. I am the folklore legend that consumes the hearts of men. I'm too much, too fast, too painful, too much to grasp. I'm the perfect woman no one wants to try or touch. I'm the beauty, the diamond in the rough. I'm the love of your life, despite the blinding nights that filled your eyes. I thought I knew true love because I held your warm hands, but you fed me lies for quite some time. You broke me down into pieces. Love was lost and here I sit.

My heart picks up and carries on thinking to land safely, free from harm. Just to dive deep into familiar seas. To dive comfortably into likened hurt, into blood that matches my bleed. Salty tears creep into the corners of my eyes when I learn one day that my perfection isn't perfect enough. And my perfect won't turn a gaze my way long enough to let me exhale and let me stop feeling this way. My perfect isn't perfect enough because the bags I carry may weigh us down. As an anchor tugs a ship, but the ship doesn't want to drown.

Someone once said to me that my beauty stopped him the moment he saw me. That my eyes and lips played in his mind. My flags went up, like bright red flowers in a field of sun. Sometimes I feel as though I am too much for a man to bear. I am an anchor waiting for a ship, but what ship wants to give up vast seas? What ship is willing to give up sailing over crashing waves just for me? I am an anchor. You can't travel to new memories or create firsts with me. I am stationary. I am whole and beautiful and steady. Just alone at sea. I am an anchor, where no one sees how heavy, my heavy makes me. Just an anchor lost at sea.

These are the unfair thoughts that I have allowed myself to think. These are the unfair thoughts that I wish to never again plague me. These are the unfair thoughts I wouldn't wish upon my greatest enemy. It's a poison that we need to rid from our bodies, to feel less than and never worthy.

September

September used to be for birthdays
A month to celebrate
Another year done
A new beginning to one

Now September is a mix of chaos and pain

I think of my grandpa
How I missed the call because I was driving
But that would've been the last time I saw his laughing, joyous face

I think of the marriage I'm supposed to be celebrating
But what joy is in a marriage that felt like a trap
What joy does a marriage hold
When it felt like every breath, I would snap

I wish I could go back
Back to when September was for birthdays

Immensely, Wholly, Beautifully

"Why don't you come to me when you cry?"

Sweet love,
I can't bear to see my pain on your face
There are questions and doubts in my mind
That I have to answer, they have to remain mine

You could love me immensely, wholly, and beautifully
But if I don't love my doubts away
Then you will be loving me in vain
It would all be a waste
Because I wouldn't feel a thing

You'd be pouring into me
As the water spills from my cracks, unknowingly

And I couldn't imagine anything worse
Than taking your love for granted
Letting you feel unappreciated
All because I couldn't let you love me
And feel it in its entirety

Because I want to love you
Immensely, wholly, and beautifully
I'd never want to drain you
Like I've been drained

Nightmares

Two AM and I am gasping for air
Because fingertips squeezed their way around my trachea
you thought you could silence me again, you dared
I went to scream for help
But you pushed hard to make sure I was noiseless and voiceless
No room to scream
Because you wanted me to listen to your manipulative apologies

Four AM and my heart is still racing
I'm turning in bed, just as my thoughts are tossing

Five AM I wake and start the day
Shake from my head the night you tried to play
Massage my neck to rid the feeling you left
Look in the mirror, see the bruises weren't there

Eleven PM
I wouldn't give you my day
The way you stole my night
But now I struggle to calm my mind

Non-reactive

You anger me
And defeat me
All in one fell-swoop

You break me
And give me the desire
To push through
In spite of you

You talk in a twisted tongue
But I am fluent

You sit there with your white flag up
Saying join me
But when I arrive
You have firearms
Fire living in your arms
Fire living in your mouth
Ready to take me out

Your fire breathing
Is no match for me
For I carry the weight of the oceans
Ready to extinguish your heat

I sway and move gracefully
And when challenged
I rise to the occasion
You can't force a reaction out of me

I'm alright

To the man
At the red light
Who looked over
And saw me cry

I just want you to know
I am alright

Happy

I am the happiest I've been in my life
I want for nothing
I crave nothing

Yet sometimes,
I still cry at night
Tears soak my pillow
For a love, that I may never know

Fly in love

I don't think I ever want to *fall* in love again
It seems like a one-sided transaction
A monthly subscription
Paying to be victim
To feelings you never actually expected

Instead, let me leap into love
Let us *fly* into love
A mutual agreement to hold each other up
A discussion between two lovers and dreamers
To always stay
The many things
That lovers and dreamers
Always dream

Falling for you
Can be beauty, like sunsets over quiet towns
But history and gravity tell me
That what goes up, must come down
Highs with you, may come crashing down
And I don't want to hit the ground

Love shouldn't keep me up at night
But let us rest peacefully
In blissful ease
Love should not have an inevitable stop
Love should be never-ending
Skies, stars, rockets, and comets
Galaxies and new life
A one-day *husband* for a one-day *wife*

My wings were melted into the wings of another. If I flew, he flew. If he fell, I fell. I was young and when young love lasts longer than two years, you know in your very naive heart that it is the realest love there is. So, when he spoke to me in ways that made me ashamed of my body, or embarrassed to be sad, I loved him anyways. I felt that the happier times outweighed all the bad. I continued to give my love to him because I was taught that love was forgiving and love finally loved me back. Then the balance shifted, and the bad times outweighed the happy times. He wasn't a bad person by any means, but I learned that the way he loved me wasn't the love I needed. I came to the conclusion that there were different types of love. There is love that comes into our body to teach us how to love ourselves, and there is love that reinforces the love we've built. It shares a home in you and never tears down the foundation you've built. The way he loved me taught me how to love myself. My first love was a lesson, and that is fine. What better gift can we receive than the ideology and initiative to begin loving ourselves the way we deserve, even if it does come at painstaking prices?

So, it begs the question, "How do you walk away from what isn't right?" When we've pledged our love and our lives to another person and have already dreamt up the future with them, how do you walk away? How do you change your future plans to no longer include the very person that you dreamt them up with?

First, something in your gut screams.
Second, you listen.
Third, you decide.

At first a quiet dull scream, because your body will know before your mind accepts it and long before your heart will act on it. In due time, your mind will exhale the plans made and stop imagining a future. In due time, your heart won't skip a beat or tremor when you hear their voice in your ear. In due time, your hands will be throwing clothes into bags and your feet will be walking away. In due time, you'll fly; a little shaky at first, but you'll be fine because your broken wings aren't so broken anymore.

I know it hurts, we have that in common. But I hope that you will find that staying in a relationship that hurts your heart will do a lot more damage than walking away from one that was never meant to last. If you look into the eyes of anyone you pass, you just might see that they share the same glossed over pain as you, because the eyes always give it away. It's okay that you're hurting, but it's not okay to let yourself continue that way. Now that you see it for what it is, you don't have to do it anymore. You can shed the burdens of someone else's pain because it was never yours to bear. Every time someone hurts you, they are projecting their fears, pain, and insecurities into your heart and tainting your soul; shake that from your head because it will only weigh you down.

Birds with broken wings call out for help,
while birds in flight just sing.
One day you will see in the mirror pain in
your eyes and feel it to your core.
One day, could be today.
One day, could come to an end.

All you have to do is decide to fly again.

CHAPTER 2

Birds of a Feather...

When a bird flies again and joins their flock, they allow themselves to be a part of something greater. Within their airborne formations they create a singular entity, where they fly on the same wisp of wind and are carried by the same air. At any given moment you may look to the skies and see birds fly, wings relaxed and soaring, taking comfort in the fact that they are not alone, for they are with their family, they have found home.

Home can be many things—yourself being the number one place where you should choose to reside. However, home can be on the backs of the ones you find most comfort in. During our fall, we may hide and push people away because we don't want them to see us covered in, *I told you so* shame. We cower down into our self-pity because it is easier than telling our loved ones, "I need help." And likely, we decide that our pain doesn't need to be placed in the laps of someone we love. We decide to remain alone in our pain so that we can save someone else from joining us as we slowly drown. Set aside the notion that in order to be strong you need to do everything on your own. Set aside the notion that help is a crutch. Your strength and beauty are going to come back to you in ways you never thought possible, you just might find that your strength and beauty never left. All you needed was your tribe to remind you where you put it.

You just may find that falling at the feet of your peers, the souls kindred to your own, is the first step at flying again. Loss, in any form, can be unbearable. So why do we try to bear it alone? Give yourself the gift of vulnerability. Give yourself the gift of feeling your brokenness in its entirety. Give yourself the gift of time to heal. Give yourself the gift of setbacks. Give yourself the gift of openness towards other people. Give yourself the gift of a second chance.

There are certain people who will touch your life in ways you never knew you needed. Without intimacy, without taking, without harming, there are people who you will find in your life that were put there to witness all that you've gone through, so that they can properly celebrate you as you exit your hardships. Brothers, sisters, cousins, parents, children. There are people who you will need. Let yourself need them while you begin the work to get back up. Let yourself fall down and trust that your tribe will protect you when you're too weak.

Maybe you will find that someone will enter your life out of the blue. I stood out in the sun and allowed myself to feel something outside of myself. I felt sunshine warming my skin and suddenly a smile crept over my face. I felt relaxed and in my skin for the first time in a long while. I hope that you allow good people in your life who will bring you that sunshine warmth feeling. It is possible to feel home in someone who was never home before. Let yourself fall into the people who let you fall deep. Let yourself listen to their words as they sound like music. Let yourself be with those who bring you comfort, safety, and calm moments. Don't hide your heart, but rather, let yourself love and live again.

Darkness & the moon

In a half-lit room
She was the darkness
And the moon

Ice cream

She grew up in a time
Where pain was handed out
Like ice cream cones
On a hot summer day

Hurt dripping down your hands
From 115-degree heat waves

I guess that's why she enjoys ice cream when it rains

Sleep tonight

I want to fall asleep on someone's shoulder
I want to get lost in their warmth
And let it lull me to sleep
Be so safe and sound
That my thoughts slow to a halt for the night
Not one race, not a single peep
I want to be held
So, I can stop doing the holding
I want to fall fast asleep
Knowing I'm not alone
Lend me your shoulder
If only for the night
Let me soak in your warmth
Help me sleep this heatless night

I will never be him

I will never be him

No matter what I do
How much I try
How hard I work
How I hide when I cry
Turn around
Greet little ones with a smile
Make dinner
Bedtime stories
Picnics

Sigh

I will never be him

My kids look past all that I do
Not out of spite
They just long for a man
Who ran from his heart
Got lost in a bottle
Called it love and swims in the shallows

I will never be him

Because I am here
And he is too far there

Run away

Take my hand
And help me run away
Hold me tighter
Take me in your embrace

I see mountains of anxiety
And piles of stress
Change the scenery of my mind
Run your fingers through my hair
Let's make a wild fucking mess

Let's run away
To our island of a bed
Take up so much space
That there's no more room for problems
Not yours and not mine
Let's clear these heads

Run away to a trail of stars
A constellation, I can see
When I trace the tattoos on your arms

Sit fireside
Cause I feel warmth when I touch your lips
And you touch my thighs

Crashing into you

I'd been walking with my head down
Eyes glued to the dirty tips of my shoes
I didn't want to lock eyes with another soul
But then I crashed into you

Broken knows broken

You said broken knows broken
Maybe that's why I say all the right things
Cause I've had my share of dark times and sunless skies
I know the feeling of endless cries

So, when I see you smile
I know its stars lining for you
I know there's up-above plans in motion
To give you sunshine and freedom highs
And I wouldn't want anything less for you

Peace in you

My soul is finding peace in you
My calm is like raging waters
Settling to a still
Drop a stone in a pond
I have waited so long
To sink heavy
And feel so rooted in you

Tell Him

I think I need to tell him
I think I need to break his heart
I think I need to shatter his soul
I think I need to give him a new start

He doesn't know my heart isn't in it
He doesn't know the ending has already happened

I think I need to tell him
Mommy won't kiss daddy again
Daddy won't share the same home
Mommy can't look dad in the eyes today
Daddy doesn't know what to say

I think I need to tell him
Mommy and daddy are done
One plus one is two
But what is two minus one?

Relax

I know your arms are tired
As strong as you are
All the weight that you carry

I know you're feeling weak
Your bones are feeling weary

Soak your mind in an Epsom salt bath
Take a breath
It's ok, relax

Fight I

Fight 'til the end of your journey
Fight to keep your blood boiling with passion
Advocate for yourself because in the end
You are all that's worth having
Dance on the tips of your toes
Crushing the eggshells you once walked around and away from
Burst through with flames
And look back at the trail you just blazed
Cross the finish line with bags of success and accolades
Because you put you first
And that's never a lost cause
Fight for yourself until the end
And every time you will win

Dude

Little boys come with scrapes and bruises
Mamas are made for kisses and soothing
Sweet boy, with golden eyes
Mama's here
You're alright

Jumping off the bed
As high as the stars are shining
My little explorer
I hope you never let the fall
Stop you from trying

Bug

She wakes before the sun
Before the dew has dried
Her hair tangled
Like beautiful forest vines
Giving life a pathway to the sky
When you see her, you begin to rise
Her eyes still sunken
Small half circles
Like the sun on the horizon
As she speaks, as she beams
You feel her light
Eyes grow wider
Smile becomes brighter

You were like poetry

You were like poetry
You ignited something in me
Like a work of art come to life
Like a song I just had to hear again
And again
And again
When you spoke
I heard music

And that's how I knew
My soul was destined to meet you

Sage and the moon

Just like sage and the moon
I find so much comfort
In you

Brown eyes

Big brown eyes
Little chocolate seas
Peeking through the door
Trying to sneak their way to me
"I just couldn't sleep mommy"
It's 9:15
You crawl into my lap
With your teddy and your tired eyes
As far as I'm concerned
This is paradise

Comfortable

The greatest comfort I've ever known
Are pages filled with poems
Surely, tear soaked
Speaking to my soul
In the dead of the night
When I'm alone

Second to the quiet nights in
Where there are no room for my thoughts
Because only you and I can fit in the bed
Being held strong enough
That I don't have to fight
Being wrapped in your courage
So, I can be weak tonight

The greatest comfort I've ever known
Is lying alongside you
Getting to be 100% vulnerable

Oh mama

Oh mama
I see your tired eyes
Waking up with the sun
And ending the day late into the night

Oh mama
Your efforts aren't in vain
Those little people love you
You can see it when they sing

Oh mama
I know sometimes you cry at night
Thinking you can't do it another second
Or that your energy is gone, and you've got no more fight

But mama
You are so much more than this moment
You are perfect, with your microwave dinners
And your yawning during play
The littles just want your time
Because that is love
And that is safe

So, rest mama
The sun will be calling in the morning
Rest
Little fingers will be reaching for you before you know it

Dreamer

I have this recurring dream
Where half my heart is found
And half my heart remains
And half my desires
Are complete in the depths of your beautiful face
Where the work to be done
Is but half a mountain to climb
Because even the tallest scales of cliff side treks
Are mole hills at best

I dream of sunsets on porch swings
Midnights and deep seeded dreams
Where my half meets your half
And I dream we've found a team
My half is your half
Sewn together at our frayed seams

If we brushed hands

If we brushed hands
And a moment was split
long minutes turned slowed time
If the stars aligned
To put your skin on mine
If an atom split
And the entire galaxy exploded
If the rain poured
And an entire forest bloomed

If we brushed hands
... would you feel all of that too

Deep brown eyes

When he looked in her deep brown
Thick like honey
Sweet like nectar
Rooted like the Earth eyes

He saw God
He saw the heavens and skies
He knew he'd never get a taste like that again
He knew he'd just been to paradise

Rather than sip the sweet nectar
Or take from the bountiful land
He only wanted to give
He wanted the beauty to blossom
So, he watered the grounds
Never taking before he gave
He asked permission to enjoy the honey
He sowed, to plant more life into her

All so he could enjoy and witness the
beauty in harmony with herself

And this is how he loved her, by letting her be

Tiptoe

Tiptoe out of bed
In the early morning light
Seeing adventure at every left and every right

Tiptoe through the mountains
Where the dinosaurs lie, sleeping at night

Two desert kids
Camping under moonlight

Somethings never change
Watching stars fly
From the road we traveled
To sights we've seen
It was all a bit easier
Because I had you there with me

At any given point in time, you may come across someone who is fighting a battle that only exists to them. The pain, only tangible to their hands, exists with such a force that it creates a pressure able to change the most hardened of people. They could be getting back up right now. Someone, somewhere, is picking themselves up off their bedroom floor in hopes that tomorrow morning the sun is shining a little bit more and feels a little warmer. Someone, somewhere, is patching up their damaged and bruised hearts, partly afraid of human contact, partly longing to be held again.

Isn't it amazing that we are in a society that moves on, while our feet are slowly getting trapped in cement? Boys meet girls and hearts break, so we grow with our insecurities and cold hearts, rather than letting them thaw. One foot races to find someone to warm the ice encapsulating our cores, while the other foot kicks and we scream, pushing away people that get too close.

They say that everyone comes with baggage. It is our own personal suitcase that houses our insecurities, our regrets and guilt, or our fears and resentment. Some bags are filled to the brim with harsh words and pained faces that we can't seem to let go of. Like a phantom pain that you cannot see—but you know it's there, because you can feel it each day—you carry bags in your hands and on your shoulders until they weigh you down and stop you from growing. From the spot where your lover grazed their fingertips along your forearms, to the very spot your lover gently pressed their lips to yours, you can feel it living on you like a vivid memory that now feels like blood clots stuck in your body. I know that those bags are as real as the people that once protected your heart, but instead, it's what you have left of them. People carry around the remains of the love they once felt, but it's the last thing that's the most memorable. It's the moment that we decide enough is enough. It's the very moment that we decided this person hurt me so badly that I won't entertain their existence in my life anymore. The last bit lives on in us and dictates our next moves. What if we take back the power and decide for ourselves what's next? All those remnants of our past, as real and beautifully tragic as they are, don't need to follow us into tomorrow.

Bags

She wore bruised shoulders through the
days and long into the nights
Lost sleep but never lost fight

Ten bags, she carried religiously
The thoughts and feelings of moments she remembered endlessly
Pick up to walk on, she shed her skin and bags fell to her feet

Seven bags, she struggled to keep tight in her grip
The memories that kept her up at night that sidetracked her steps
Pick up to walk on, she shed her skin and bags fell past her hips

Three bags, she held tight to
But quickly realized, in the home she built, there was no room
Put down and sit still, like the air she could breathe in
These bags did not belong to her anymore
Though they've provided walls while weathering storms
They were burdens that were not hers

Zero bags, her hands were freed
Bruises healed
Now empty hands to take on glistening new things
Now empty hands
No weight to bear, now just breathe

I wish to find words

I wish to find words
That fit your face
And fit your beauty
And fit your grace

I wish to find words
That spoke volumes to the way you make me feel
The way you turn rain showers into May flowers
The way you turn clouds to shaded areas perfect for
picnics and quick dates on our lunch hour

I wish to find words
In which the sounds of glory and hallelujah
washed over me the first time I saw a choir
That sounded like birds chirping in the morning dew hours
Like harp strings plucked, melodies turned
stories from the first time we touched

I wish to find words, that did you justice
That measured up to your eyes and where your love is
An 8th wonder of the world, number 1 where I'm
concerned, I wish to find those kind of words

San Diego

Heat warms the tips of our toes
As we sit in a circle surrounded by people
who share the same scarred bones
But it wasn't the mutual pain that filled the space
It was the affirmations and smiles that flew
on the backs of embers that day
Each were lit like a Northern star
Each one directed me home when I seemed to stray too far

I could look into each of their eyes
And see stories of triumph and fight
In each of their eyes,
Scarred tissue from tears cried
In each of their eyes,
Love, hope, and dream filled skies
In each of their eyes,
Were lights beautifully bright

But it was this night
Looking around the fire
Cheers to the skies
And cheers to each other
Tears swelled the corners of my eyes
I've never felt so safe being so close to fire
I've never felt such bliss
And I know I'd never been higher
Here with my tribe, I've never felt so inspired

I know it feels like life can tear you down, but I also know that you have it in you to get back up. Although we've never met, I know that about you. But, until you can find that residual strength, just know that there is a tribe of people that you can lean on. Find refuge in your family, your friends, your book club, your gym mates, or sports team. Find refuge in a therapist or group of like-minded people. We are social beings. It is our biological and psychological nature to group together for safety and security. I ask that you give yourself the chance to be vulnerable and need your tribe.

I know it's always easier to focus on someone else so that you can take your attention off of the hurt you've been left to heal; even though you didn't cause it. However, let's not forget the importance of focusing your attention inward. Ignoring your pain will not erase it, it will only prolong it. As much as we all may need other people, never forget that you are a person that you must learn to live with and rely on. This is because only you can heal yourself, only you can decide that you are worth more, and only you can change your circumstances to receive all that you deserve. You are just as much a part of your tribe as your mother, who looks at you with wide and tearful eyes wishing so desperately to take away your pain. You are just as much a part of your tribe as your siblings, who grit their teeth and tighten their fists when they hear what made you cry. You are just as much a part of your tribe as anyone else. Treat yourself the way your best friend would, dissect all that caused you pain and speak encouraging words long through the night while melting into a bowl of soul-healing ice cream.

~~~~~

You dared to bite into love's fruit and decided to love fearlessly and without restraint, but it bit back. You still have to get up because you deserve to get back up. You deserve to love fearlessly and without restraint, and you deserve for it to love you back this time. Love will not be in the eyes of someone else this time. Love will be in the family that surrounds you. Love will be in the way you marvel at their
~~~~~

strength. Love will be the way you applaud their successes. Love will be the way you stick up for yourself. Love will be the way you throw a right hook when life takes a swing at you. Love will be the way you fail but keep going. Love will be in the people who need you and who deserve your love. Love will be in the people who remind you to love yourself too and don't ask for anything in return.

Look to them, look to your tribe, for you will marvel at their light. You will be inspired by their creative and decisive ways. You will try to match their relentless and courageous behavior, all the while, they are the ones inspired by you and they are the ones cheering you on and trying to match your grit and strength.

Today, I invite you to put down what does not serve you, put it down, and never touch it again. I dare you to find reason within yourself to feel and live again. I dare you to let yourself be vulnerable. Step outside and let the sunshine thaw your cold shoulders. Breathe in the crisp morning air and let nature live in your bones again. I dare you to allow your body to feel rooted into the Earth so that your soul may find peace. There is no constant in your life path like that of your connection to the universe, so I dare you to feel that connection and embrace it.

It is quite euphoric when you are able to feel again, and I mean really feel, when your smiles are no longer forced and you are no longer reaching for a hand or waiting for your voice to be heard. Look back on the progress you made with respect to where you are now. Look at how you have loved yourself enough to sleep at night, rather than let your anxieties and fears keep you awake. Look at the smile that you wear now and feel the wrinkles it's pressing into your face. Rather than parading around wearing a mask and being the person that you wish to present to the world, allow yourself in all your flaws and glory. Feel how you're able to press the resentment out of your body, evicting it from your emotional abilities. I hope you love every bit of who you are. I hope that you discover that your biggest and brightest dreams contain the person you are today. I hope that you don't shy away from being your authentic self.

It's possible that we may never forget the things said to us, the deterrents that stood in our way, or the way it felt to sink into depression despite being in a room full of people. It's possible that sometimes we will lie awake at night after living through another nightmare. Our minds are complex, and we can't fight the occurrences within ourselves to nonexistence, but we can combat them with new practices. We can say to ourselves, going forward, that we are worthy. When nightmares shake us to our core, we have the power to center ourselves and push forward.

My greatest wish for others, my greatest wish for you, is that you also never forget that you are love in its purest and truest form. You have everything you need within you. It's a wonderful comfort to have family and friends remind you who you are. And it's a wonderful joy to be reminded that you have lightning, and you have thunder, therefore, you are the storm. However, it is an even greater comfort and joy to remind yourself of those things.

~~~~~~

I am strong.
I feel determined.
I can do anything with confidence and grace.
I love wholeheartedly.
I speak my truth unapologetically.
I know and trust my intuition.
I am the divine being in which I seek.

~~~~~~

CHAPTER 3

Renewal in the Silence

Solace is the moment where peace and clarity resume in your life. It is the moment we search for and hope for but can never attain. This is because solace is not a destination, but a realization. It is realizing that everything you have ever needed resides within you. It is realizing that peace and calmness is as easy to find as it is to spot a bird in the sky. You have such magnificent power and abundance about you, there can never be something that could make you crumble. Just as the day you were born, you were not influenced by the praise you constantly got. The adornment you received did not make you a better infant, it did not add to your magnificence, you just were. You were already at peace and at ease because all you ever knew was all that you were, and all that were, was alive. You screamed to the world because your infant heart had something to say. However, your infant heart never needed validation from anyone else to exist peacefully. You just did. Just as we are here and now, not needing validation or praise to exist in peace, you just can. Solace is there, it never left you.

You will live in solace after you have endured rain for so long that you forgot what it means to be dry and warm in the comfort of your own home. You will find comfort after your lungs have been cleared from thick smoke that suffocates your airways. You will know solace after feeling the end of your world and deciding that you never want to give someone else the power to destroy you like that again. You will know solace when you decide to cleanse your life of people and things that suck the energy out of your soul. Like a bright light that you never knew existed, in a tunnel you never knew you were trapped in, you will see an illuminating change. When people experience heartache and pain to such a devastating extent, something changes within us, it is up to us to decide if that change can be purposeful or let it tear us down further. It is the oddest phenomenon that our pain blooms beauty, so long as you let it. What once felt like bruised bones, no longer strong enough to carry our weight, let alone our burdens, now feels like a second wind. Before we know it, our minds decide to flood life, love, and art back into us. I believe that when you pour love into yourself a weight is shifted off your heart. Suddenly, you sit in amazement at how far you've come. Confidence in your decisions replaces the smoke in your lungs as you stand firmly in your beliefs and transitions.

We dreamt of days where crying only occurred because we clutched our bellies as we laughed too hard. We could only fathom the day our screams would occur because we lived life to its full exhaling excitement and relief into the universe. In solace, we will find that we are able to shed our hesitations and fears. We don't have to live with skepticism and shallow breathing, waiting for someone to remove the anvil that once sat on our chests.

Now, you can strip yourself of the things that you do not need. You have the chance to shed your skin of all the things you feel no longer serve you. You have the power to rid yourself of society's toxic expectations and the words they spat at you that made you feel less than. Like you're in a hot shower, let the hurt wash off your skin until all that's left is you and solace will resume.

Inhale

Inhale
The air fills my lungs
And my posture corrects itself
My head gets closer to the clouds
But I only feel more grounded
What a beautiful thing
To let the mind and body mingle
Until they sing

L-O-V-E

Somewhere along the lines
It felt like the way you loved me changed
L-O-V-E
Replaced with another 4-letter word
That can only be felt deeply
And burns with a passion
Immense and pure

I saw it in your eyes, like I once saw love
I saw a sea of emotions
I saw resentment and fear
Like a soup to feed the soul on a rainy day
Your eyes held bits and pieces
That fed the hate

You looked at me with disgust
You looked at me like I threw away your trust
You looked at me and your eyes spat in my face
All I could feel was shame and disgrace

One day your *L-O-V-E*
Turned into *H-A-T-E*
But I'm learning the hate wasn't towards me
You hated you, and that's not my burden to carry
You hated you, so now I *L-O-V-E* me

Sky's Garden

How lucky are we
That the sky mistakes us for flowers
And decides to water our flesh
And rain life into us
So that we may breathe again

5 minutes

Give me five minutes of your time
So, I can see the light behind your eyes
The cracks behind your smile
And the pause in your spine
Everyone sees how strong you carry yourself
But show me the ways you fall
Show me what breaks you
And how we can move that stagnant angst
Into a purposeful crawl
Hold on to me
As tight as you please
Relax your jaw, let the tension ease
Let's fill your spine with strength
And get you off your weary knees

What is done in love

What is done in love
May be the purest of things
For it comes from a place of longing, yet certainty
It was birthed in chambers that no one has seen

What is done in love
Is a creation that fed on vulnerability
Hand crafted with honest-filled eyes
Wrapped in tender-loving, humbled tries

What is done in love
Messy, somewhere between quick and slow
Is a language all in its own
Where nothing sounds sweeter
Than your lips smiling the word hello
No guilt, fear, or words to rescind
What's done in love is where I want to live until time's end

Our song

Fast forward
Five years, maybe ten
Early morning
We're late for work and the kids are late for school
The dogs are barking

But our song comes on
And suddenly, the whole room is stopping

Time stands still
Everything is frozen
Except your hand, reaching for mine
The glimmer in the corner of your eye
The spin I make in two-seconds time

Hand on your chest
Head tilted high
Exhale
I kiss your smile

4 minutes and 18 seconds go by

Neptune

Let's travel the galaxy
Surf the stars, all the way to Neptune
Let's dance in the diamond raindrops
So, we can be around skies as beautiful as you

Existence

To exist alongside you
Would be the thing of dreams
For you are the one whom my soul has prayed for
And my heart sings

Each dream, I dreamt a faceless mystery
Who brought me peace and love
With every touch
Each intention was set to manifest my heart's equal
Each time and every night
My thoughts would race to find you at the finish line
So, when our hands touched, I knew your
face was missing from my vision
You were who I prayed for
And when my heart sang your name in its beat
I knew you and I were meant to be

Excitement and longing fills my aches
Because it feels like the mirror of my soul ran into me today
And sees their home in my eyes
His dream home is me, this he will decide
His eyes show my home, a place I've longed to reside
I may never blink again
Not today, nor the rest of time

Sunflower

Love me strong
Like a sunflower that has weathered a desert storm

Love me beautifully
Like a dewy sunflower glistening each morn

Love me abundantly
Like the plentiful seeds

Love me carefully
Brazenly, yet tenderly

Ladylike

My mother raised me to be ladylike
To bat my eyes and be polite
Don't speak of personal matters
But tonight, I might
Just let my imagination run a little wild
Cause when I think of you
I don't picture sitting still
Or smiles painted on faces
Coy and shy
I think of biting your lips
Your tongue on mine
Hearts racing and tingling places
Straddle your body, getting ready for a ride
Feeling the strength of your wood
Pressed against my thighs
I want to taste your pride

I like when your hand finds a place on my chest
Your hands, big and firm
Sit heavy on my clavicle
Gentle and warm

You make me moan and praise gods I barely know
Flip me over and stroke 'til I feel it in my torso
You like to see the arch in my back
As I grab at the sheets and bury my face until I need to gasp

Then I'll ease back into ladylike
Oversized t-shirt over my shoulders
And peek-a-boo thighs
Throw my tired leg over to your side
Hand and head over your chest
You took me from fuck me to tired eyes
Adrenaline slowed, back to ladylike

Solace I

Leap
Swan dive into your soul and explore depths
Let yourself root into your being again
Feel the strength fill into your bones once more
The adrenaline from excitement towards
life rushes through your veins
From your crown to your toes rooted on the floor
As you exhale the smoke and inhale all the beauty that you are
Solace exists
In you and around you
Solace is you
So, leap

Stop Time

Detach from the notion that you are your past
Your present self didn't ask for that
Respect your being in this moment's time
Respect that the future is not to be defined

We are beings dictated by time
But if man made it
We can change it
Take back the clock
Take back the racing to your next stop

And stop

Come back
To this moment's breath
The crisp morning air
Come back to now
The past is done
There's nothing to be done
The future can wait
Come back to this moment
Come back to today

Home

I remember the feeling of home
When I sat in the sky
Curled up in a star-studded throne
Heat from sun's rays
Engulfed me and held me
From moment to moment
Warming my bones

The lack of gravity
Lifted away all stressors
It was here in this moment
I felt clarity and ease
Surrounded by stars
I've never felt so much peace

Breathe again

When purple and pink streak through the sky
And palm trees stand tall despite storming nights
After rain, sleet and snow have taken flight
I find such a calm when I look up high
Crisp air to fill my foggy lungs
I know anything before, and anything done
I will breathe again
Because the sky doesn't lie
Just as the sun sits up high
Trees live for me and through me
I am apart of Earth's cycle, just like the moon
Therefore, each new day
Can never be a day too soon

Dandelions

Pick up a dandelion
And blow on its seeds
Watch them fly away in the wind
As you drop the stem
One story ends
But new life takes root
A new wish for a new day
A new dream for you
One small moment to hold such promise
Such desperation and longing
To put all hopes and dreams
On the backs of wingless seedlings

Colorado Springs

There's a place
Where the sun peaks from in between buildings
To create one small sliver of warmth
A spot I like to visit each morning

It's as if standing here is my way of being with her
She wakes me and speaks through the bird's chirping
Her sunny rays kiss my cheeks
Her warmth ignites my soul
Until tomorrow morning, this feeling I'll hold

Sunset Beach

The beach sands cling to my toes
Like a heavy weight and burden, I cannot shed
Then the salty ocean waters
Push forward and cover my soul
Lie those burdens to rest
I stood before those mighty seas
Seeking peace and clarity
It gave me so much more
Because it took the pain
Cleansed the wounds
And left me feeling free again

Solace II

Somewhere, far away
Rests a woman with a smile about her tired face
She lies down at the end of the day
Muscles don't ache and bones don't suffer sprains
She is able to pause after she conquers the day

I wish you words

I wish you the words that are too hard to speak
The moments that pull you back
When you've been nearing the brink
I wish you calm
Amongst your wave swallowing storms
The daybreak each morn
I wish you peace
Despite people stealing that very thing

Ready, Set... On 3

I'd say
I want to know you on the deepest of levels
I want to know where all the pain lives, to this day
So that I may dedicate the rest of my life to kissing it away
I want to hold your big, warm hands
And navigate life together
You got my 3 o'clock and I got your 9
Hands intertwined, until the end of time
Together we stand, side by side

I want to be held accountable
For the words I spill
I want to love and resolve into the early morning lights
I want to always be standing on the same side of the fight

I want a team out of you and me
Four kids
Long nights
I'll jump if you jump with me
Excited smiles
Ready, set… on 3

We do this together
A leap of faith so happily
A family built in holy matrimony
I know your fears and concerns
I know you hold years of hurt
Fresh soil, new roots, flowers bloom from dirt
We could start a garden together
Watch life unfold together
And flowers bloom forever

Fall in love in music each day
Like the first time I hit play on that song Major sang
"This is why…" I'm sure you already know
You are who I choose, each day that we grow

I got your 12 and you got my 6 o'clock
Forever stand behind you
Arms wrapped around you
Giving you love, support and all of me
To keep you strong, whatever you need
Each day, this journey I wake to see
Each day, ready to leap

I'll jump if you jump with me
Excited smiles
Kiss me quick
Ready, set… on 3

If you must look back on your life, if your thoughts retrace the steps of moments cried, be present enough to understand that moment is gone. The moments that we imagined defining us are only a mirage now. Every single moment we've ever endured was only relevant to our existence at that time. Those memories and events are as real as a movie, in that, they are just scenes replaying in your mind. As far as this moment goes, your past is irrelevant. It carries no weight, because with or without those experiences, you have the power to dictate your next step. Looking back only prevents you from living out your life now.

Time is a man-made creation that lingers over our head and dictates our thoughts. With time, we constantly get lost in *that one time.* We struggle to figure out if we are on time, and we stress over the time-lines that we set for ourselves, but we don't have to do that. We can look in the past with respect to how far we've come and where we are at now. Better yet, we don't have to look back at all. There is not one moment of the past that can be changed, so, harboring negative and painful thoughts about what happened does nothing for you, except allow you to carry that burden. You can decide to put down any and all past hardships. It is a foreign concept, but it is possible. If you want a chance at solace, I believe that you need to make peace with your demons and set them free. After all, they are only demons because we have held onto those memories and kept them hostage in our minds for so long. If you were held hostage, you'd go crazy too. So, let them go, for they are figments of the past, and the past no longer exists now.

When you find the strength to invest in yourself and love yourself with a courageous force, you will receive that love back. All your hard work will come to fruition in the form of peace and happiness. When you get to such a point in loving yourself with all of your imperfec-tions and insecurities, when you love yourself despite the harmful things other people have said to you, you open yourself to receiving that love back.

Should you decide to look towards the future, do it sparingly. There is no need to cause yourself anxiety and pain over what has yet to come. Let go of the expectations of tomorrow and let go of the expectations you set for other people. Plan your future but plan it for yourself. Plan it for your children. Plan it for your peace. Understand the difference between expecting a certain outcome and striving for certain goals; understand that shortcomings are inevitable, and that is okay.

If, and when, you decide that you want to invite love back into your life, then be open to love shared. For as long as you can, stay in the moment, stay present. In your body, the home you've built and perfected, you have everything you need. You have a life of love and contentment if you so choose to create that space. The greatest loss we can suffer is losing ourselves before ever having the chance to truly live. Remaining open to positivity and new chances is not easy after experiencing a mentally, physically, or emotionally abusive relationship. It's not easy to walk around with a pained heart after loss of any kind, but I believe that staying open to opportunity and possibility can save you. Being hopeful about something can save you. I find it very important to reiterate that you are already love, in and of itself, there is no outside source that can make you feel more whole than you can. I also understand that to be able to share your heart with someone is a beautiful and magical thing. I hope you love yourself enough to remain open to the possibility that someone may love your heart and all the remnants of the hurt that you've kissed away. Skepticism may cloud your vision, and when it does, take a step back and look at things from a new perspective. Keep choosing yourself and keep giving yourself chances to be open to life.

CHAPTER 4

Freed Bird

First heartbreak. This phrase carries such a succession throughout our lineage that we believe it is a coming of age to have experienced love, and again, to have experienced love lost. It is the human way to discover love outside of ourselves and it is the human way to be so terribly destroyed by it that we no longer recognize ourselves in the mirror. Since when is that okay? Since when is it okay to barter our self-love for that of the temporary boost of serotonin and affection provided by someone else? How did we ever fathom the idea to exchange what is already owned?

The world tells us from an early age that love is from someone else. The world tells us that love is to be found, to be searched for, and then to be shared. What the world failed to tell us is that love runs through our bodies, just as the water we carry or the food we eat. Love is inside our blood vessels and bones, waiting to be recognized by its host so that it may dance around your soul and sing to you. When should we ever trade our own self-love songs for that of another's affection? That'd be like trading your water for someone else's food, when you need to hydrate, and they are too hungry to last the day. Hold on to your love and your light and let them keep theirs. Love is when two fully intact people come together with enough water in their bodies, food in their bellies, and light and love in their bones and blood vessels. Together they feast, as they are not sharing a meal for one person. Together love floods, as the water source within them never runs dry. Together, love carries their muscles and bones as they raise their arms and extend their gratitude for one another. Heartbreak may, very well, occur at any given time; but love will never be lost again, as you will learn, it is in you. It is around you. It is you.

You are love.

Like nature

Like a flower struggling to break free from toughened ground
And roots reaching to their survival
I persevere through any tribulation
From tests turned trials

Like birds soaring and falling mid flight
They catch on the wings of their feather friends to fly again
I rise and I fall, I break then bleed
Yet, I fall into love of warm souls, kindred to me
I soar again, forever soar freely

Like waves, pushing and pulling with the strength of the moon
Nighttime beckons and anger swells
Crashing on sandcastles built by small hands
I, too, roar to the world in the deepened night skies
I, too, carry my rage until it towers over, and I cry
Wet eyes washed away like waves crashed to Earth's clay
I calm like morning waves
Soft on the shore, under warm sun rays

I may fall into darkness
I may cry until I melt
I may struggle to be free
But each dawn
Each light
Each movement before taking flight
I get back to the tips of my toes
I reach for stars in sight
Despite being distant from my body, but known to my soul
I go further and reach higher
See brighter days
Like nature, I breathe it all
Like nature, I am okay

Kitchen floor

I used to sit on the kitchen floor
Of my too small, overcrowded
Two-bedroom apartment

I used to cry and cry and cry
On that floor
I used to curse the world
I used to ride out my anxiety attacks
And sink deeper into my depression
I used to give up
And take the punches that life was throwing my way

And you used it all
You threw that in my face

Now I sit on the kitchen floor
Of my too small, perfectly spaced
Nothing out of place
One-bedroom apartment

And I thank the stars
That I got up and walked away

I wanted me back

Today I ended an era
Finished a book and set it down
No intention of reading it again
Today I ended a relationship
Where two people met and became one
Grew distant and became two
Grew distant and stayed distant
My pain is not obvious
But the burden I carried from it
Was all too present
My pain was not set on a shelf for all to see
But tucked away under my pillow
Surrounded by a pool of tears cried each night
My pain was ever present
Evergreen
Like a well-watered forest
Each tear, the life given to a budding fear and break
My pain was a forest

But I searched for a galaxy
I wanted to see my reflection and see the
stars that I knew lingered within
I wanted to sit amongst my brothers and
sisters with flames about my grin
I wanted to feel as bright as they come
I wanted me back
For I am the sun
I want to sit so high that nothing can bring me down
I want to sit among the clouds
I want to hear birds sing me their songs
And smell flowers as I walk along
I wanted me back
For the rest of my nights, and the rest of my mornings

Fight II

When your bones hold too much ache to rise
At least hold your head high
When the tears are weighing down your neck
At least crack open your eyes
Let the light in

Fight for you the way you fought to save what broke you
Advocate for you
Fight for you
Love you

Let light touch you
Let light embrace you
Let light engulf you

Until the tears don't weigh you down
Until you can lift your head
Until your bones don't ache
Until you can rise again

When you find yourself taking the blame for too many things, I wish you the strength to peel open your eyes and see what is not warranted. Every fight resolved by your apology is more than likely an unfair fight. Do you really think that everything stems from your actions or that you are to blame? Let those painful words slide off your back as they aren't yours anymore. Yes, everyone has their faults and should apologize when those faults hurt someone else. However, know when the line is being crossed from owning up to your mistakes, to being manipulated into taking ownership for someone else's mistakes. People should strive to hold themselves accountable for their actions. In unknown and subconscious ways, we project our pain onto other people as a defense mechanism. These are things that everyone should make note of for their own account, so that we do not cut people with the same knives that shed our blood.

So, I wish you the insight to see when someone is smearing their blood and pain onto you. As well as the insight to know when you're doing the same. People can be so scared that they carry their hurt without thinking about it, and without a second thought, they end up using their own pain as a weapon. I wish you the guts to put an end to it, so that you may never suffer at the hands of someone else again. I wish you the guts to stop your own cyclical patterns that force you to react out of pain. When you break the cycle, you are freeing yourself of future hurt. Break the pain cycle in yourself, and it stops the pain cycle *outside* of yourself by no longer allowing others to mistreat you. No one deserves that pain or that responsibility. No one should yield that type of power; the power to take someone down so swiftly and easily.

Forgive yourself for being human and acting in error. Forgive yourself for sitting and accepting the words someone deemed fitting for you. Whatever the case, forgive yourself so that you can heal within and stand tall again.

Forgiveness

I always wondered and question
Why is forgiveness to be given
To those who forgot to give
Why do we spend so much of our lives
Giving someone else peace of mind
From those times
That they ripped our eyes from their sockets
And blamed us for being blind

Why do we forgive someone else
When it doesn't actually heal, and it doesn't actually help

I imagined that forgiveness was like a light
Something you give someone when you're tired of the fight
You hand over a clean slate, shiny and bright

I believed that when you forgave someone
You weren't allowed to be hurt by it
So that's why I never quite allowed it
Because I knew I'd constantly doubt it
I knew that I could never clean the slate
That stolen food would reveal the crumbs left on the plate
And stolen moments would leave me with hate
That I'd miss the shine of the sky
That I'd never stop questioning why

So, forgiveness, I never gave

Until I realized one day
It was never a gift we mistakenly give away
Forgiveness is what you bestow upon yourself
It is the mindset of allowing yourself to heal

It is telling yourself lullaby's in the mirror
Forgiveness is what you do when you apologize to you
For not sticking up for yourself when you should have
Or warming your bones when you were shivering blue
Forgiveness is letting your heart stay open
When someone tries to melt it shut
It is opening your eyes again
After your eyelids were sewn shut

It is not using the blade that sliced your delicate skin
Against the likes of many innocent men
Forgiveness is gifting yourself love and patience
Forgiveness was never a gift for the monsters that tried to eat us
It was never some glowing orb gifted to
those who would mistreat us

Forgiveness is not painted in the frowns of obligation
It does not belong to people for the sake of peace making
Forgiveness is yours
The benefit of the doubt
The love beneath your pillow
The tea that warms your mouth
It is the persistence that you deserve to carry
The do-overs that we give too freely
It is the second chances that you should have given to yourself
It is your peace
And your mind
It is your healing
And re-drawing those fine lines

All these years, I never knew forgiveness was mine
Now I give it freely, I forgive myself all the time

You matter

You matter
In ways you don't understand
And don't yet believe
You matter
The way it matters that rain waters the trees
Your soul, hand-stitched by stars in the sky
Who sacrificed bits of their own shine
To make you perfectly, just in time for your arrival
Your soul matters
The way your smile adds light to your eyes
Or your presence equates to paradise

Hair dye

Today, I wash the color from my hair
I wash away the impulsive decisions
To change my life
And to change my mind

I cried and cried for something to give
So, I went to the store
And bought boxes of dye
Thinking this small change would make it all so much better
That I wouldn't want to die

So, I colored, and I changed
And life was great

But like band aids
The knock off kind that never actually stick
The color was only a temporary fix

I see my hair and multi-faceted tones
As a representation
Of an unhappy home

But today, I don't need it
I cut away the dead ends
Natural brown hues
Like earth and sand
I feel so grounded
Here I stand
No dye, not dying
Because I changed the inner view

Capital R

We met in bits and pieces
I collected your soul in small moments of time
Like vines, you hung around me in the
crowded forest I called a home
You introduced yourself to me
But I hid you away
And collected your character,
What choice did I have when you came in so brave?
You grew and grew
Until it was only you and I in this big, crowded room

And here you are, still by my side
Like a friend I never asked for
Yet, you hold my deepest worries and in you I confide
I've never touched your skin
But rather, a piece of you, my heart resides in
Your red hot keeps me warm on already summer days
Your strong, tightening fingers, hold me tight in your embrace

A capital R, your name plays in my head
Resentment, why do I lie with you in my bed?
I toss and turn to find my other lover, Anger, over my shoulder
When Anxiety is lurking from around the corner
We live, like a loud quartet, screaming awful melodies
In this small and crowded home
For years, the four of us, is all that I have ever known

But I'm ready to move on
I can't stand the way you shape my words and hurt
So, this life I have come to know
I stand and light fire to this home
Where the four of us have lived
From children to full grown
My soul is mine and you can't have what's left
You three, are the only thing left for me to resent
If I could, hold you in the palm of my hands and
crush you until you crumble to pieces
I would, and then smile as your ashes blow away in the wind
Hoping that you would catch fire, again and again

I get to build a new home
The ashes have blown away and I dance alone
The walls are no longer present
The smell of sunflowers replaces the memory of the crowded home
And I finally have fresh air to
Inhale
And exhale
From my once stuffed nose
I'm hearing birds chirp for the first time
And my peaceful soul is happy in its brand-new home

Self-love

There's something about loving yourself
It is hard
And it is painful
It feels wrong
But baby
It is so right
Because you'll never feel your bed too empty at night
You'll never need the arms of another to
warm you or calm your frights

You'll see that when you let love in
It will be because you desire someone, not who you need
It will be because you are ready to share
your peace with another being
You won't need anything from anyone
Because you are already whole
You are already one

Never say never

Never say never
Except when never is the key
And I mean to your well being
There are things you should never do
Never let someone take away your peace
Never put yourself down when you were meant to fly freely
Never say yes when your heart is screaming *NO!*
Never agree to be an option, when baby,
you're the prize and the show
Never believe you're less than
Because you are so much more
Sometimes, say never
It's not a bad word
It's a boundary
And never is the door

My love is mine

My love is mine
What I have to give and share
Is merely the excess
The overflow of what is already there

When you look at me
You'll see a freed bird
Dancing, from flower to fruit
In need of nothing
All happiness, no pursuit

And because my love is mine
I can let you in
I choose to share my love
I want to share my time

9:00—5:00

When a 9 to 5 becomes a 7 to late
When carrying your family exhausts your brain
When being a man all day long
Forces you to be cold and not to feel
Know I'm here waiting for you
With open arms and love to heal
I'll run a hot bath
You take off the armor and shield
I see you, soul first
No forcing or faking here
Love sacrifice and heart bleed
I'll take care of you as you do for me
As a Queen does for a King

Midnight tides

There can never be a day when I regret melting into your skin
Or feeling warmth from your face
There will never be a day
That I wish to run the opposite way
As there is, and always has been
Something about you
Like I was the midnight tides
And you were the moon
Something about the way you pretend not to stare
Something about the way you always show you care
Something about the way you remind me you'll always be there
Like pulling waves ashore
Like pulling me to you
I will always be your midnight tides
Ever longing for, ever admiring you

Priceless

Do not put yourself in a position
That you cannot afford
My mother spoke those words so often
It became a part of our home decor

So, I ask you
How easy is it to replace your peace?
How easily can you afford
To walk down to the store
Aisle 10
And ask the clerk
But he responds,
"Sorry, for we are all out
Peace is not for sale anymore"

So, when you let them talk down to you
Degrade you
And berate you
You allow them to steal away at bits of you
And steal away your peace
You allow them to take
The very thing you cannot afford to lose
The very thing you cannot replace

When they eat at your soul
Or chip away at your shoulder
Stand tall and strong
You deserve to walk away
Those feelings are not yours to harbor
Without question or answer
Walk away
Kick up dirt with your shoes
Because peace is too priceless
And your peace belongs to you
This, you cannot afford to lose

So, I ask you
Can you afford to be without peace
When your existence depends on that very thing

Never again

Lying in bed
It's 12:30 at night
Contemplating the past two months of my life
I've been my best and my happiest

Never again will I shrink to fit in
Never again will I apologize to end the fight
Just for the sake of ending the fight
Just for the sake of saying you're right
Just for the sake of saying good night
Just for the sake of being your wife

I came here with a backpack and ache
I came here and I stayed
Never again will I step back into who I was
I have asked the universe to send me something to relieve my pain
Send me something to help me abstain from being drained
Send me something
Something

I was vague in my needs
I was messy in my desires
So, the universe conspired
Rather than giving, took me away
Placed me on a clean slate
Said *"my darling, you'll know what to do.*
Those feet of yours will hit the ground running
As soon as you come to."
The universe conspired
The universe provided
The universe woke me up
And for that, I will never be sorry

I fell in love with you

I fell in love with you
The way I fell in love with music
Because all at once, you hit all five senses
I hit play and allowed you in

The gum rolling in my mouth, suddenly strong bursts of mint
The colors before me, vivid and distinct
The smell of sunflowers under the morning sun
The hairs on my arm raise to attention
Welcoming your touch
The sound of your melody captivating me, engulfing me
The way I fell in love with you
Was all at once, and suddenly

Power

Don't you know that you hold the power?
I call to you in this 6 o'clock hour
Heated water to wake your tired face
Let the steam wash away doubts of yesterday
Find the fit that makes you feel most at home
Throw your shoulders back, walk confidently to your throne

The soles of your shoes will have conversations with the floor
Excited and elated
To hit the ground running, once more
Fate lingers
Wondering when to tempt you best
To see if you're serious about this foolish quest

But you have the power
I scream it at you
My voice turns spirit
Let it burn from me through you
Never let that slide past you again
You have the key to destiny
To this story, you hold the pen
You decide if, who, what, where and when
Your voice, mightier than any demon
Your stride lights a fire to halls you've walked in
Your mind sets people straight
and at you, they admire in
Aspire in
They take notes to be like you
they fill their shoes to try and match your stride in
A feeble attempt at replication
Don't you know you hold power?
People aim to be you, Look at them.

So, pick yourself up
Shake that resentment and guilt from your head
Throw out the doubt and unjustified feelings
The only thing you're doing with it
Is distracting your mind
You put up a wall that separates you from yourself
That holds you back from being your very best
Live with your negative and tell your power to send a message
Don't wait 'til the day is over
Do it now, in this 6 o'clock hour
Let it say, chest broad, confident, and unafraid
I've got work to do, you can stay, or you can be on your way
But either way, my power overpowers you
Either way, my agenda is the only thing on today's to-do
Either way, my wants take precedent
Because my wants take care of me and you
Let your power say one more
Either way, I'm good without you

Don't you know you hold power?
Why let it fight for attention
With insecurities and neglect
When neglecting your power
Is feeding into a dark frenzy

Give in to your power
Let it resonate with your soul
And marinate in your bones
Give rise to your voice
Light up your home
Give in to your power
Walk taller and plan accordingly
Wake each day
Look forward to it, consciously
You have within you a storm
Tear that town down
Rebuild and make it yours

Don't you know you hold power?

Lovers & Dreamers

To my lovers
My dreamers
My hurt ones
My secret keepers

For the beautiful people who have felt the desire to scream
For those who struggle to find their voice
Or those who have just been newly introduced
Done are the days where we sit idle
Letting others get by with murder while we sit afraid
Done are the days where we quiet our voices
To keep the room from catching aflame
Done are the days when our throats burn with rage
Because we chose to keep quiet
When we should have spit fire
And should have broken hell
And should have thrown glass
When we should have yelled

We are not mice anymore
We are the flamethrowers

To be in love can be a beautiful thing. To find art and love in the eyes of another can be a mental vacation from all the life you've endured. I hope you find love as solid as the foundation that you've built in your soul. The foundation being the tears you've cried mixed with the fights you've won to cement yourself whole again. Rooted in yourself and love rooted in you.

I hope you never settle for a love that gives you a vacation. I believe that love is a mirror, and when you look in their eyes you should feel at home. You should feel their heart when yours beats and you should feel their hair rise as you touch their soft skin. I wish you a love so deep and profound that it cannot be spoken into words so easily because they just wouldn't do it justice. I hope love weakens the toughened walls that life forced you to build. Something about the two of you should stop the chaos that flies around your day, because something about the two of you sounds like ocean waves, calm and gently existing in harmony. You two are waves working together, pushing, and pulling off the shore. A gentle kiss as the waves go from a tall crash to a delicate covering of your toes when they're cold.

Imagine being in sync with each other because you two are made from the same star having been destined to be one from the moment it fell, and dust scattered over the world creating you two in different places. The same bits of the universe live in each of your veins, ensuring that you two would live a glorious path to coexist once again. That is the love I wish for you. I whole-heartedly believe that once you have found solace within yourself and doused yourself in love, you will have found the stars and they will have found you.

~~~~~

One day you may wake up and want love in your life that was specially designed for you. Should that day come, I hope that you find yourself whole and able. My greatest wish for you is that you sit with your spine so strong and your smile so wide, that nothing and no one can take it away. I hope that you understand how much you have
~~~~~

earned that strength in your backbone. You have earned that love that you chose to direct inward. I hope that one day, when the time is right and that moment comes, that you find someone who compliments your strength, because they, too, fought and earned their own. Most of all, I wish that when you want to find love again, they never challenge your strength and never try to weaken your spine because love is strengthening in nature.

I dreamt of the day where my soul is full, and my heart is content. I dreamt of the day where happiness is truly unconditional, not tied to anything or anyone. Lastly, I dream of the day in which I can share that joy with someone else.

These pages may not hold the words that you so desperately needed to hear; "I love you" from his lips to your opened ear. In any case, I hope it spoke to you, if only to let you know that you are not alone. If only to hold your hurt or serve as open hands where your tears may fall. I hope that here, in the pages where we met, I was able to provide you hope and strength.

~~~~~

The journey we all take, to and from heartbreak, is a blurry line only recognizable by feelings and time. I'm asking you, a patron on the side of the road, heed my words and venture into the unknown. If, at any point in time in your life, you have felt that something was not right or that you deserved more, don't wait to find out, take your strength and head to the door.

A wild detour, I urge you to take, where you lift from the ground and begin to fill your heart today. You have everything you need within your chest and your head; you have everything inside you to pick yourself up again.

You are beautiful beyond measure with a soul meant to shine. You were handcrafted by the stars; this is why you shine so bright. You are worthy
~~~~~

of all the love and light in this world. You are not destined for pain. If someone treats you like you are less than, that is a direct reflection of their own insecurities and darkness within.

~~~~~

When love finds you, let it find you whole. When love finds you, may you be so open that you're able to accept it in its most raw form. When love finds you, may your vision be cleared from the last storm. When love finds you, may you muster up the courage to greet it with *hello.*
~~~~~

Epilogue

My own story continues in these pages, and many others. I go through ups and downs because I still find it difficult some days to maintain my own anxiety and depression. However, now that I have less pain in my life, I don't struggle in the same ways. I have set boundaries for myself as a woman in ways I never knew that I could. I never had my voice before, but now that I do, I see no reason to hide amongst what does not serve me. I feel confident in my decisions and actions in a freeing and unapologetic manner.

I try my hardest not to lose sight of the true goal. My goal is to be a better and brighter me only for the sake of myself. I have been hurt, but that does not mean I have to carry that hurt. I have been scarred, but that does not mean that I have to carry those scars. I have also been loved. I have two beautiful children that shine light through their eyes. I would give anything for them, especially a loving and dedicated mother. So, I am doing the inner, personal work to be the best mother I can be for them.

I become tiresome and irritable, but I know that is not a reflection of who I am as a mom or person. I know that the words my ex-husband said were out of anger and his own pain, and they hold no truth to my character. Lastly, I know that I am deserving of so much more than I've ever been dealt. I deserve a forgiving and honest love. There is no better person to give that to me than myself.

I forgive myself for ever taking blame in a situation that was no fault of my own. I forgive myself for staying quiet when I had plenty to say. I forgive myself for staying in a relationship that wasn't good for me mentally or emotionally. I forgive myself. I have concluded that, while he is not an awful person, he didn't know how to love me correctly. He had his own insecurities that he pushed on to me. He was a jealous man, and so, a lot of things came down to my appearance or my actions because he felt any changes were a sign of my infidelity, which he manifested in his own mind and implied in passive aggressive ways. At the end of our decade long relationship I believe he lost sight of the woman I am and all that I can offer. I am a home and I am beautiful, and my body is perfect the way it is. There has never been a malicious bone in my body, but he saw me through fogged lenses and that is not my burden to carry.

None of this excuses the way things unfolded, but it also gives me perspective that helps me move forward. He was but a pained man, speaking and existing from a place of pain. I cannot hold that against him. Rather, I can only hope that he will love himself enough to free his own heart of hurt and be a better man for himself. I wish him happiness and love in the future.

If you take anything from my journey, I hope it is that you are a worthy and loving individual. You deserve all the light and love in the world. I hope, more than anything, you find it in your heart to give yourself those very things. I hope you feel that you don't need someone else to whisper sweet nothings in your ear to feel validated. You are a strong, amazing person. Your hurt doesn't have to hurt anymore, and you have the power to walk away from amazingly difficult situations.

Don't let someone take away your power. When you feel weakened and defeated, find that one last morsel of strength and rise. No one has enough power to strip you of your grit and might. Never let someone else take from you, and then trick you by calling it love. Never let someone else take advantage of your heart and your soul. Never let your loved one gloss over your pain and call it irrational. Those are not things to settle for just because they have come to love bits and pieces of you.

You have everything you need within yourself.
You are love.

Lightning Source UK Ltd.
Milton Keynes UK
UKHW040636080321
379977UK00001B/24